Reinhold Moritzevič Glière

Two Pieces
Zwei Stücke

for Double Bass and Piano · für Kontrabass und Klavier

op. 32

F 95085

ROB. FORBERG MUSIKVERLAG

INDEX · INHALT

Cover image · Umschlagbild: M. Čiurlionis, *Sonata della Stella. Allegro* (1908)

F 95085

ISMN 979-0-2061-0619-4

Two Pieces · Zwei Stücke
Prélude

Reinhold Moritzevič Glière
op. 32/1

4

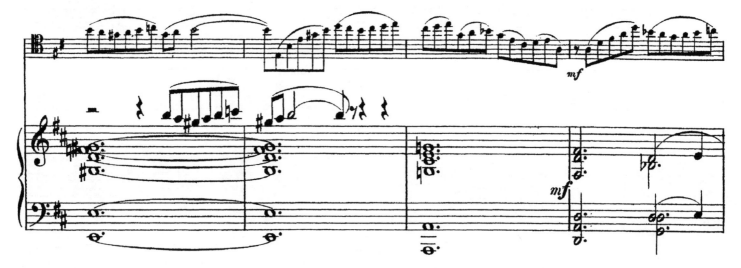

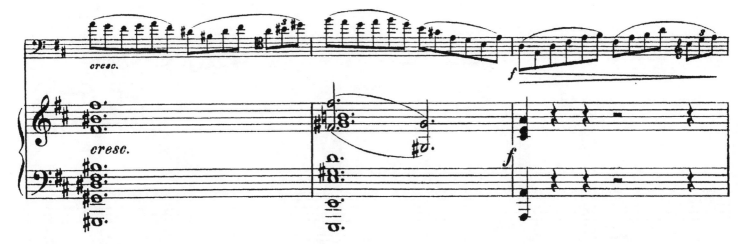

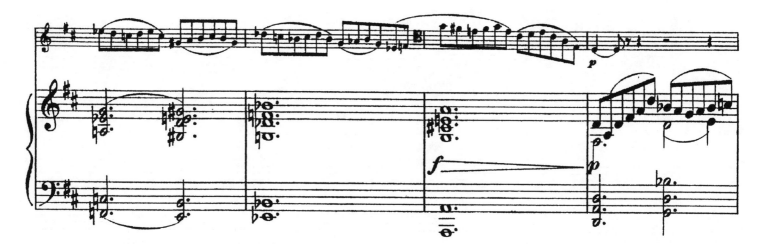

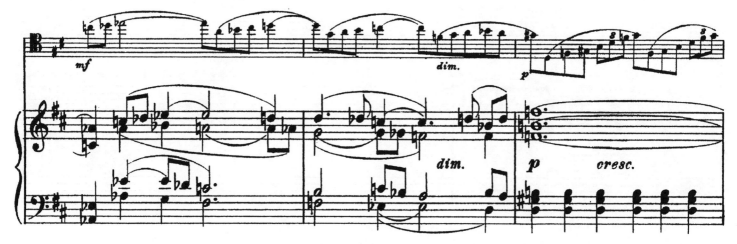

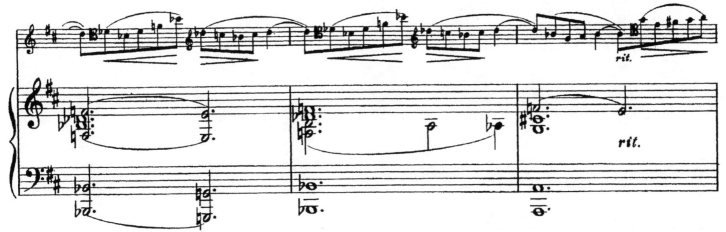

Scherzo

op. 32/2

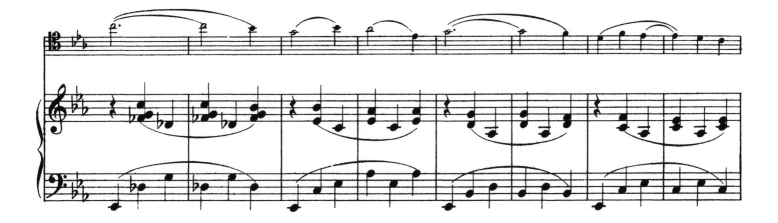

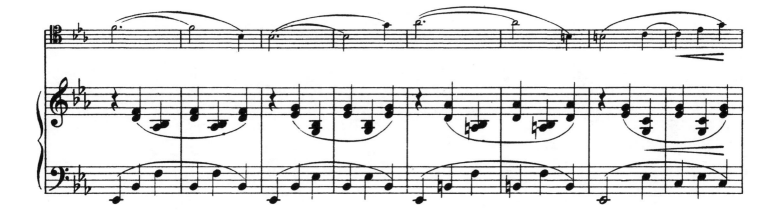

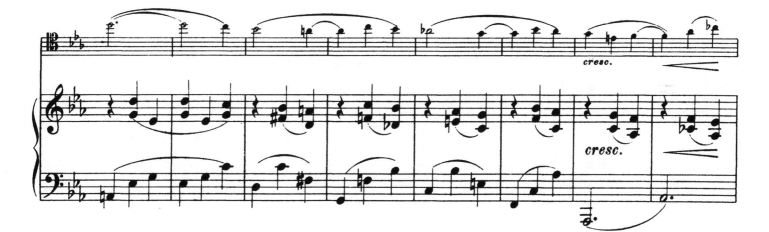

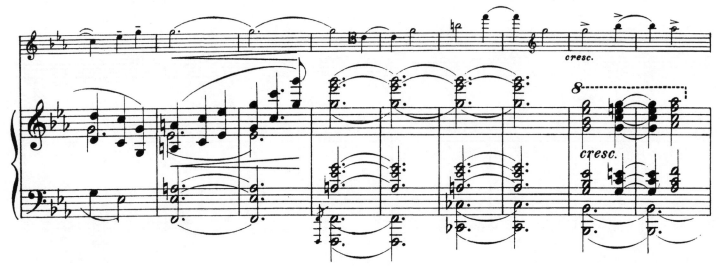

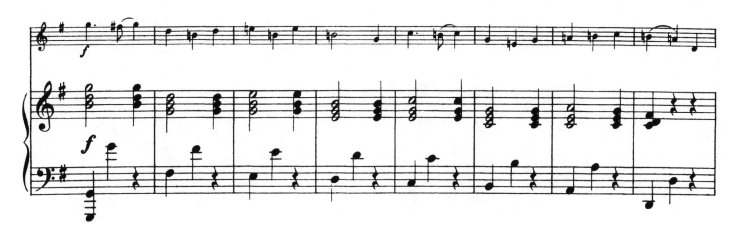

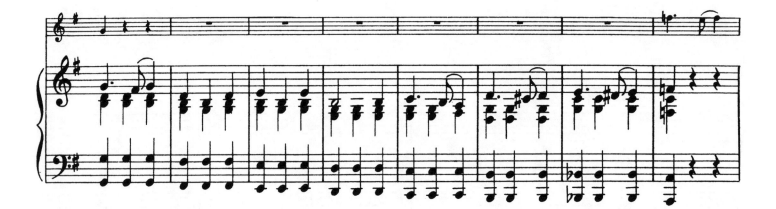

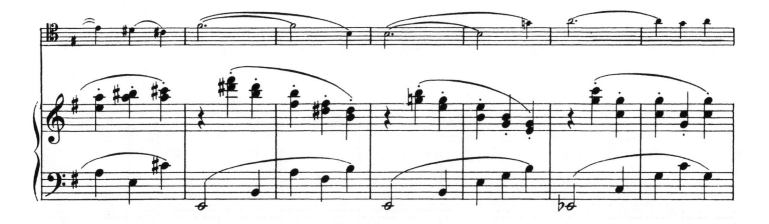

Reinhold Moritzevič Glière

Two Pieces
Zwei Stücke

for Double Bass and Piano · für Kontrabass und Klavier

op. 32

KONTRABASS

F 95085

ROB. FORBERG MUSIKVERLAG

Two Pieces · Zwei Stücke
Prélude

Reinhold Moritzevič Glière
op. 32/1

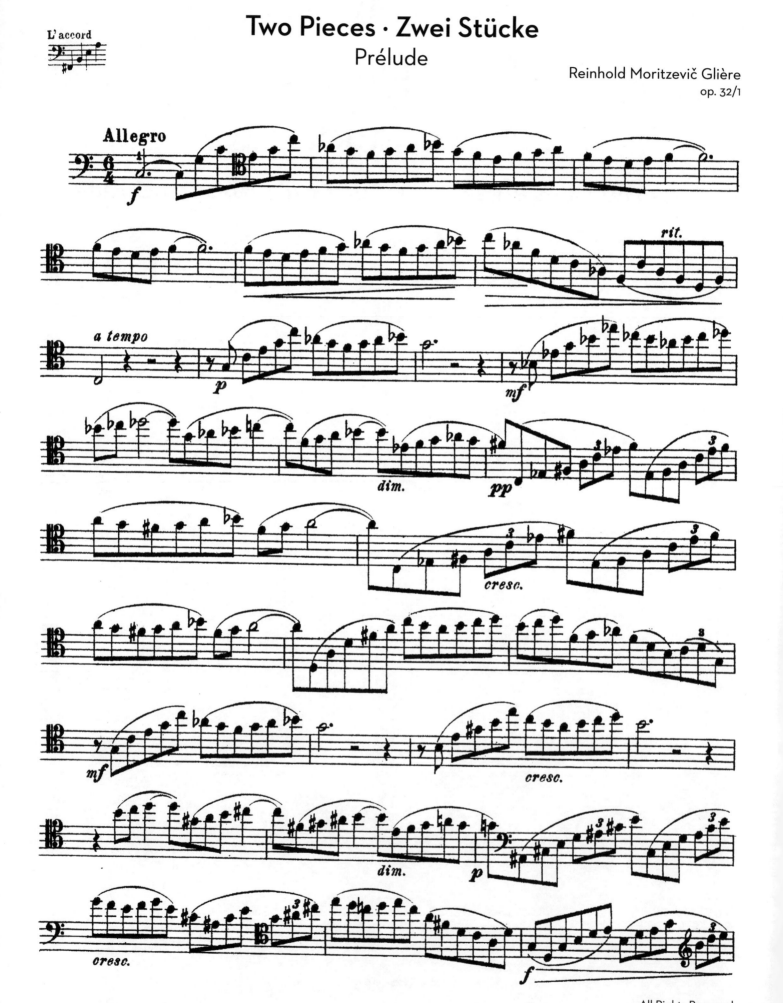

Scherzo

op. 32/2